VISTAS

An Interactive Course in English

WORKBOOK

3

Project Director H. Douglas Brown

Writer
Marjorie Fuchs

Regents / Prentice Hall
Englewood Cliffs, New Jersey 07632

Publisher: Tina B. Carver
Manager of Product Development: Mary Vaughn
Senior Editor: Larry Anger
Development Editor: Tunde A. Dewey
Managing Editor, Production: Sylvia Moore
Design Director: Janet Schmid
Interior and Cover Design: Suzanne Bennett
Pre-Press Buyer: Ray Keating
Manufacturing Buyer: Lori Bulwin
Scheduler: Leslie Coward

Illustrators: Don Martinetti, Alex Mizuno, Ellen Sasaki, Arnold Ten
Cover Photo: Freeman Patterson/ Masterfile

1993 by Regents/Prentice Hall
A Simon & Schuster Company
Englewood Cliffs, New Jersey 07632

Printed in the United States of America
10 9 8 7 6 5 4 3 2 1

ISBN 0-13-650375-6

Prentice-Hall International (UK) Limited, *London*
Prentice-Hall of Australia Pty. Limited, *Sydney*
Prentice-Hall Canada Inc., *Toronto*
Prentice-Hall Hispanoamericana, S.A., *Mexico*
Prentice-Hall of India Private Limited, *New Delhi*
Prentice-Hall of Japan, Inc., *Tokyo*
Simon & Schuster Asia Pte. Ltd., *Singapore*
Editora Prentice-Hall do Brasil, Ltda., *Rio de Janeiro*

CONTENTS

EXERCISE 1

Look at the information about Victor Sanchez. Then complete the conversation.

Last Name	*Sanchez*
First Name	*Victor*
Address	*293 Bolton Ave.*
	Dallas, TX 75229
Place of Birth	*Spain*
Married	Yes ✔ No

Secretary 1: His first name's Victor, <u>*isn't*</u> <u>*it*</u>?

                                                      1   2

Secretary 2: _____ , _____ _____ .

          3   4   5

Secretary 1: What's his last name?

Secretary 2: Sanchez.

Secretary 1: That's S-A-N-C-H-E-S, _____ _____ ?

                                           6   7

Secretary 2: _____ , _____ _____ . It's S-A-N-C-H-E-Z.

          8   9   10

Secretary 1: Oh. He speaks Spanish, _____ _____ ?

                                        11   12

Secretary 2: _____ , _____ _____ . He's from Madrid. He's only been here a few days.

          13   14   15

Secretary 1: He lives on Bolton Street, _____ _____ ?

                                      16   17

Secretary 2: _____ , _____ _____ .

          18   19   20

Secretary 1: Hmmm. That's near me. He seems very nice. He's single, _____ _____ ?

                                                                        21   22

Secretary 2: _____ , _____ _____ . His wife is still in Spain.

          23   24   25

Secretary 1: Oh, well.

Look at these hospital rules. Then complete the sentences with *may* or *may not*.

```
┌─────────────────────────────────────────┐
│              HOSPITAL RULES               │
│                 No Noise                  │
│      No Smoking (except in room 10A)      │
│     No Food or Drink (except in cafeteria)│
│                No Animals                 │
│            No Children Under 12           │
│      Visitors 10:00 - 12:00 and 4:00 - 7:00│
│      ❋ ❋ ❋ ❋ ❋ ❋ ❋ ❋ ❋ ❋ ❋ ❋            │
│          Information at Nurses' Desk       │
└─────────────────────────────────────────┘
```

1. You *may not* make noise in the hospital.

2. You _____ smoke in the patients' rooms.

3. You _____ smoke in the cafeteria, but you _____ smoke in room 10A.

4. You _____ visit patients at 9:00 A.M.

5. You _____ visit patients at 1:00 P.M.

6. You _____ get information at the nurses' desk.

7. You _____ bring your 10-year-old son to the hospital to visit a patient.

8. Teenagers _____ visit patients.

9. You _____ bring flowers to patients.

10. You _____ bring a cat into the hospital.

What are some rules in your school or library? Write sentences with *can* or *can't*. You can use some of the ideas in exercise 2.

1. *You can't smoke.* _____

2. _____

3. _____

4. _____

5. _____

6. _____

Complete the conversation with *for* or *since*.

Marie: How long have you been in the States?

Victor: ___*For*___ two months, but I've only been in Dallas _____ last weekend.
          1   2
          What about you?

Marie: Oh, I've been in the States _____ 1983.
                                          3

Victor: Have you always lived in Dallas?

Marie: No, I've only been here _____ 1984.
                                      4

Victor: How do you like your job at the Language Institute?

Marie: I like it a lot. I've worked here _____ six years.
                                                5

Victor: That's a long time. Have you studied any languages here?

Marie: Yes, I've studied Spanish _____ about nine years and French _____
                                        6   7
          1984. What about you? How long have you studied English?

Victor: Oh, I've studied English _____ a long time.
                                        8

Marie: Well, your English is very good.

Victor: Thanks.

Find the past participles of these verbs. The words go →, ↓, ↗, and ↘.

| be | come | go | ~~live~~ | meet | study | work |

```
A  C  E  M  I  T  S
D  O  G  L  A  L  E
A  M  T  O  B  I  N
S  E  R  T  N  V  N
S  T  U  D  I  E  D
W  O  R  K  E  D  N
N  E  S  B  L  A  T
```

Make questions with these words.

1. How long / you / live / here?

   How long have you lived here?

2. How long / Victor / study / English?

   _____

3. How long / he / be / in this English class?

   _____

4. How long / your teacher / work / in this school?

   _____

5. How long / Marie / work / in the office?

   _____

6. How long / you / be married?

   _____

Now answer the questions in exercise 6.

1. _____

2. _____

3. _____

4. _____

5. _____

6. _____

EXERCISE 1

Look at these pictures. Make sentences with *used to* or *didn't use to*.

1. Lucy / live in Mexico

Lucy used to live in Mexico.

2. Lynn / have short hair

_____

3. Pravit / ride a bike

_____

4. Roberto / swim at the beach

_____

5. Victor / read the newspaper

_____

6. Gina / dance

_____

EXERCISE 2

What about you? Complete these sentences. Use your own information.

1. When I was younger, I used to _____ .

2. When I was younger, I didn't use to _____ .

Complete the conversation. Use the correct form of *used to* and the verbs.

Keiko: What do you think about the new student in our class?

Gina: Victor? Oh, he seems very nice. And his English is really good.

Keiko: Yes. When he was younger, he ___*used to go*___ to American movies and he also
1 go

_____ an American pen pal.
2 have

Gina: _____ they _____ their letters only in English?
3 write

Keiko: Yes, they did. All the time.

Gina: What else do you know about him? Where _____ he _____
4 live

when he was little?

Keiko: Well, I know his parents are in Madrid now, but he _____
5 not live

there. I think he _____ in the country, but I'm not sure.
6 live

Gina: What _____ he _____ in his free time? Do you know?
7 do

Keiko: He _____ to music a lot and learn all the American
8 listen

hit songs.

Gina: Great! Maybe he can teach us some!

EXERCISE 1

Circle the correct words in parentheses to complete the sentences.

My friend Renato (**1.** (is) / has been) from Brazil. He (**2.** has lived / lived) in São Paulo (**3.** since / for) all his life. Renato is an engineer. He (**4.** has been / was / were) an engineer (**5.** since / for) ten years. He (**6.** speaks / is speaking) English very well. He (**7.** studied / has studied) English (**8.** since / for) high school.

Before he got married, he (**9.** used to visit / visited) the States very often. He (**10.** has been / is) married (**11.** since / for) three years now and (**12.** hasn't been / wasn't) in the States (**13.** since / for) then.

He has many hobbies and interests. He (**14.** has been / was) interested in water sports and soccer (**15.** since / for) his childhood. When Renato (**16.** was / has been) eight years old, he (**17.** can / could) already water-ski. He also used to (**18.** play / played / playing) soccer with his friends, but now he doesn't.

EXERCISE 2

Do you remember? Answer these questions. Then look at page 8 in the Student Book and check your answers.

1. Could Pravit speak English when he was little?

   No, he couldn't.

2. Could Olga?

   _____

3. What about Keiko?

   _____

4. Susan?

   _____

5. What about you?

   _____

Use the phrases below to ask questions about the pictures. Use *could* or *couldn't*. Then give short answers.

1. use a computer / secretary

   A: _Could the secretary use a computer?_

   B: _No, he couldn't._

2. drive a truck / she

   A: _____

   B: _____

3. play tennis / they

   A: _____

   B: _____

4. speak English / he

   A: _____

   B: _____

5. swim / boy

   A: _____

   B: _____

6. count / children

   A: _____

   B: _____

7. ride a bike / she

   A: _____

   B: _____

Look at Lucy's job questionnaire.

Job Questionnaire

How do you feel about these things? Check the appropriate box.

I	love to	like to	don't like to	hate to
1. help people	[✔]	[ ]	[ ]	[ ]
2. work alone	[ ]	[ ]	[ ]	[✔]
3. have a lot of responsibility	[ ]	[✔]	[ ]	[ ]
4. work in an office	[ ]	[ ]	[✔]	[ ]
5. answer the telephone	[ ]	[✔]	[ ]	[ ]
6. travel	[ ]	[ ]	[✔]	[ ]
7. write letters	[ ]	[ ]	[✔]	[ ]
8. talk in front of many people	[ ]	[ ]	[✔]	[ ]

Now write sentences about Lucy. Use the gerund (verb + *-ing*).

1. *Lucy loves helping people.*

2. _____

3. _____

4. _____

5. _____

6. _____

7. _____

8. _____

Complete this job questionnaire. Use your own information.

Job Questionnaire

How do you feel about these things? Check the appropriate box.

I	love to	like to	don't like to	hate to
1. meet new people	[ ]	[ ]	[ ]	[ ]
2. wear a suit	[ ]	[ ]	[ ]	[ ]
3. stay at home	[ ]	[ ]	[ ]	[ ]
4. learn new things	[ ]	[ ]	[ ]	[ ]
5. speak other languages	[ ]	[ ]	[ ]	[ ]
6. get up very early	[ ]	[ ]	[ ]	[ ]
7. take care of other people	[ ]	[ ]	[ ]	[ ]
8. have a routine	[ ]	[ ]	[ ]	[ ]

Now write sentences about yourself. Use the gerund (verb + *-ing*).

1. _____

2. _____

3. _____

4. _____

5. _____

6. _____

7. _____

8. _____

Read this school newspaper article about Victor Sanchez. Complete it with *a* (only if necessary) or the prepositions *to, at,* and *in*.

Meet Victor Sanchez

Victor Sanchez, from Madrid, Spain, is ¹ _a___ new student here at the Language Institute. Victor has only been in the States for ² _____ few months, but he already likes it. Victor is married and has ³ _____ daughter. His family is still in Spain and Victor is looking forward ⁴ _____ seeing them soon.

Victor has many interests. He loves ⁵ _____ music. He plays the guitar and he's interested ⁶ _____ starting ⁷ _____ band. So, if you're good ⁸ _____ playing ⁹ _____ musical instrument, speak to Victor.

Victor is also very interested ¹⁰ _____ meeting new people here in Dallas and visiting ¹¹ _____ lot of places in the States.

Nice to meet you, Victor! And good luck!

Complete this chart.

Gerund	Base form
1. enjoying	*enjoy*
2. _____	travel
3. _____	drive
4. writing	_____
5. filing	_____
6. _____	sit
7. _____	be
8. cooking	_____
9. _____	have

Look at the pictures and complete the sentences. Use *to*, *at*, *about*, and *of* if necessary.

1. She enjoys *taking pictures* .

2. She can't stand _____.

3. She's looking forward _____

_____.

4. He's good _____

_____.

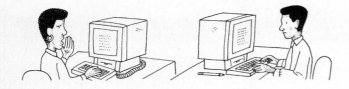

5. They're tired _____

_____.

6. He's thinking _____

_____.

7. He hates _____

_____.

8. I'm worried _____

_____.

What do these people do? Look at the pictures and write what you think. Use *must*.

1. He _must be a doctor_ .

2. They _____ .

3. I _____ .

4. She _____ .

5. You _____ .

6. He _____ .

7. We _____ .

8. You _____ .

9. They _____ .

10. She _____ .

Match the first half of each sentence on the left with the reasons on the right. Use *could* or *couldn't*.

because

e 1. He *couldn't* be a pilot,　　　　　　a. he can't type.

___ 2. I _____ be a taxi driver,　　b. she's good at numbers.

___ 3. She _____ work as a cashier,　c. they love helping people.

___ 4. He _____ be a computer　　d. she hates to cook.
　　　 programmer,
　　　　　　　　　　　　　　　　　　　　e. he's afraid of flying.

___ 5. They _____ be nurses,　　　f. he's good with his hands.

___ 6. He _____ be a carpenter,　　g. they don't enjoy working outside.

___ 7. She _____ work as a chef,　h. I don't have a driver's license.

___ 8. They _____ be farmers,

Write statements about these situations. Use *must* or *must not* and the words in parentheses.

1. Pierre got a 55% on his English test.

   (very happy) *He must not be very happy.* _____

2. Lucy worked all night.

   (tired) _____

3. The audience hasn't laughed at all at the comedy.

   (funny) _____

4. Roberto hasn't eaten anything all day.

   (well) _____

5. Mrs. Brennan's father is 70 years old, lives in Florida, and plays tennis every day.

   (retired) _____

6. I asked the question three times, but the woman didn't answer me.

   (English) _____

Read this letter from Keiko's friend. There are ten mistakes in it. Find and correct them.

Dear Keiko,

   I just received your last letter. Congratulations! You must ~~to~~ be very happy with your new job! I know you have always been interested in to work with a fashion designer. With your business background you could doing a lot of things. But this job sounds perfect for you.

   I still hate my job. I can't stand be in the office all day. I enjoy travel, and I want to meet new people. Perhaps one day I could be travel agent. I think I'm good in talking to people, but I still need to improve my English. I am tired at doing the same thing every day. I hate routines!

   Well, I want going to the store now before it closes.
   I look forward to see you soon.
                    Love,
                    Umm

Unscramble these words. They are all adjectives that describe people's personalities.

1. giagsrvees   A (G) G R E S S (I) V E

2. taptine   _ _ _ (_) _ (_) _

3. drefyiln   _ _ _ _ (_) _ (_)

4. nopserlibes   _ (_) _ _ _ _ _ _ _ _

5. labileer   _ (_) _ _ _ (_) _

6. pinedeendnt   _ (_) _ _ _ _ _ _ _ (_)

Now unscramble the letters in the circles to spell another "personality" adjective.

7. _ _ _ _ _ _ _ _ _ _ _ _ _

Write about the kind of job you would like. Use the information from the job questionnaire that you completed on page 10.

_____

_____

_____

_____

_____

_____

_____

_____

_____

_____

_____

_____

EXERCISE 1

Complete Angela's letter to Gina. Use the verbs in the box.

buy	find	live
come	~~get married~~	see
do	have	tell

Dear Gina,

Congratulations! I'm so happy for you. I think it's great that you and Frank plan **¹ to get married**. Of course, Jim and I promise **² _____** to the wedding! In fact, we can't wait **³ _____** you again. It's been a long time!

Where do you expect **⁴ _____** after you get married? Is Frank's place big enough or will you have **⁵ _____** a new apartment?

I remember when I got married. It's difficult. I know you'll probably need **⁶ _____** a lot of shopping for your new home. Jim and I would really like **⁷ _____** you a special present. Any ideas?

I think it's good that you decided **⁸ _____** a small wedding. Small weddings are less impersonal.

Well, I'm really looking forward to getting the invitation.

Love,
Angela

P.S. Don't forget **⁹ _____** me what you want for a present!

What do these two people plan to do before their wedding? Look at the pictures and write sentences.

1. _They plan to buy wedding rings._

2. _____

3. _____

4. _____

5. _____

6. _____

Write sentences about yourself. Use these verbs: _decide, need, prefer, expect, hate, continue, want._

1. _I decided to go to the movies._ _____

2. _____

3. _____

4. _____

5. _____

6. _____

Look at the pictures. Write what each person has *just* done.

1. Jim *has just met Mrs. Johnston* .

2. Tina _____ .

3. She _____ .

4. He _____ .

5. He _____ .

6. They _____ .

7. She _____ .

8. She _____ .

Look at Gina and Frank's list of things to do. Then complete the telephone conversation with the correct form of the verbs and *already* or *yet*.

TO DO
find a place for the wedding reception
buy invitations ✓
mail invitations ✓
hire a band
buy wedding dress ✓
buy wedding rings

Mother: So, how are things going?

Gina: Oh, pretty well. We've done a lot, and our friends are helping us a lot.

Mother: That's good. I know you don't like organizing parties. Have you ___found___ a
                                                                                           1 find
place for the reception _____?
                              2

Gina: No, but we're going to look for one this weekend.

Mother: What about invitations?

Gina: We've _____ _____ and _____ the invitations.
                    3   **4** buy   **5** mail
You should get one in the mail very soon.

Mother: Have you _____ a band _____?
                         6 hire   **7**

Gina: No. My friend Lynn is going to do that.

Mother: And what about your wedding dress?

Gina: I've _____ _____ one, and it's beautiful!
                    8   **9** buy

Mother: Oh, I'm so happy for you! It's going to be a wonderful wedding.

Gina: I'm sorry, Mom, but I have to go now. I still have a lot to do. Frank and I

haven't even _____ our rings _____!
                 10 buy   **11**

Mother: OK. Good luck. I'll speak to you later.

A week before Gina and Frank got married, Mrs. Brennan's English class had a wedding shower for Gina. Look at the table at Gina's wedding shower. Then complete the conversations with *some*, *any*, *a*, *one*, or *the*.

Pierre: Is there ___*any*___ champagne?
　　　　　　　　　　１

Victor: Yes. I couldn't find _____ Spanish champagne, but I got _____ French
　　　　　　　　　　　　　　　　　　２　　　　　　　　　　　　　　　　　　３
　　　　champagne. Would you like _____ glass?
　　　　　　　　　　　　　　　　　　４

Pierre: Sure, I'd love _____ .
　　　　　　　　　　　　　５

Victor: How about you, Yon Mi?

Yon Mi: Thanks, but I don't drink champagne.

Victor: Well, there's _____ soda, too. I'll get you _____ .
　　　　　　　　　　　　６　　　　　　　　　　　　　　　７

Lynn: _____ cake is great! Have you had _____ ?
　　　　　　８　　　　　　　　　　　　　　　　　９

Keiko: I had _____ before. It *is* delicious, but I think I'll have _____ fruit now. Are
　　　　　　　　　１０　　　　　　　　　　　　　　　　　　　　　　　　１１
　　　　there _____ more bananas?
　　　　　　　　　１２

Lynn: Yeah. I see _____ in the bowl.
　　　　　　　　　１３

Gina wrote her friends a note to thank them for the wedding shower. Complete her note.
(∅ = no *the*)

Thank you for (**1.** (the)/∅) wonderful party! I still can't believe it! (**2.** The/∅) food was great, especially (**3.** a/the) cake. And (**4.** the/∅) French champagne is my favorite drink!

I've (**5.** already/yet) gotten the pictures back. They're beautiful. Especially (**6.** the/a) one of me and Frank next to (**7.** the/a) living room table.

Thanks again!
Love,
Gina

Circle the appropriate response.

1. Would you help me organize my party?
   a. Sure.
   b. Yes, please.
   c. Yes, I do.

2. Have you told your family yet?
   a. Yes, I did.
   b. Yes, I have.
   c. Yes, I will.

3. You must have a lot to do.
   a. Yes, I must.
   b. Yes, I do.
   c. Yes, I will.

4. Congratulations!
   a. You're welcome.
   b. Thank you.
   c. Please.

5. It's a great cake!
   a. Yes, a cake is delicious.
   b. Yes, the cake is delicious.
   c. Yes, cake is delicious.

6. I'll buy the soda.
   a. Thanks.
   b. Yes, you will.
   c. Sure.

7. Have they ordered the food yet?
   a. No. They ordered it two weeks ago.
   b. Yes. They're going to order it tomorrow.
   c. No, they haven't.

8. Would you like some cake?
   a. Yes, I do.
   b. Yes, please.
   c. I like cake.

Look at the invitation. Write *That's right, That's wrong,* or *It doesn't say.* Correct the sentences that are wrong.

YOU ARE INVITED

To ___*A Wedding Shower*___

For ___*Gina Poggi*___

On ___*November 2nd*___ At ___*7:30*___ o'clock

At ___*Lynn and Keiko's, 431 Lincoln Street, Apt 4*___

R.S.V.P. ___*555 - 8133*___

---

1. This is an invitation to a wedding.

   That's wrong. It's an invitation to a wedding shower.

2. Gina is going to get married.

   _____

3. The party is on November 22nd.

   _____

4. Lynn and Keiko have the same address.

   _____

5. The party is going to be at school.

   _____

6. Lynn and Keiko want a response to the invitation.

   _____

You are organizing a party for your husband, your wife, or a good friend. The party is going to be at your home. Complete the invitation. Use your own information.

YOU ARE INVITED

To _____

For _____

On _____ At _____ o'clock

At _____

R.S.V.P. _____

Complete the conversation with the appropriate words.

Gina: I'm nervous. Do we have everything? Have you _**bought**_ the champagne _____?
1   2

Lynn: No, we _____ . We're going _____ it tomorrow.
3   4

Gina: _____ you ordered the food yet?
5

Lynn: Of course, we _____ . We ordered it two weeks _____ .
6   7

Gina: What about glasses? Have you bought the glasses _____ ?
8

Keiko: No. I'm going to get them when I buy _____ champagne.
9

Gina: Have you _____ the decorations yet?
10

Lynn: Yes. We've _____ gotten the decorations. We _____ them yesterday.
11   12

Gina: Have you _____ the band yet? _____ you ordered the cake?
13   14

Lynn: Yes. We hired the band last week and _____ the cake two weeks _____ .
15   16

Gina: Let's see. Is there anything else? Oh, yes. _____ you gotten the rice?
17

Keiko: Rice?

Gina: Yes. You know. It's traditional to throw rice at weddings in the States.

Keiko: Oh. Well, no. We _____ gotten _____ rice yet.
18   19

UNIT 4

EXERCISE 1

These people are invited to a wedding. What might they buy as wedding gifts?

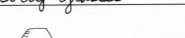

1. He *might buy glasses* .

2. She _____ .

3. He _____ .

4. He _____ .

5. They _____ .

6. They _____ .

7. He _____ .

8. She _____ .

EXERCISE 2

Look at the pictures in exercise 1. Have you ever bought any of those things? Write about each picture. Follow the examples.

1. *I've never bought glasses.*
   I've bought glasses many times.
   I bought glasses five years ago.

2. _____

3. _____

4. _____

5. _____

6. _____

7. _____

8. _____

Look at Ann Brennan's passport. Then complete the conversation.

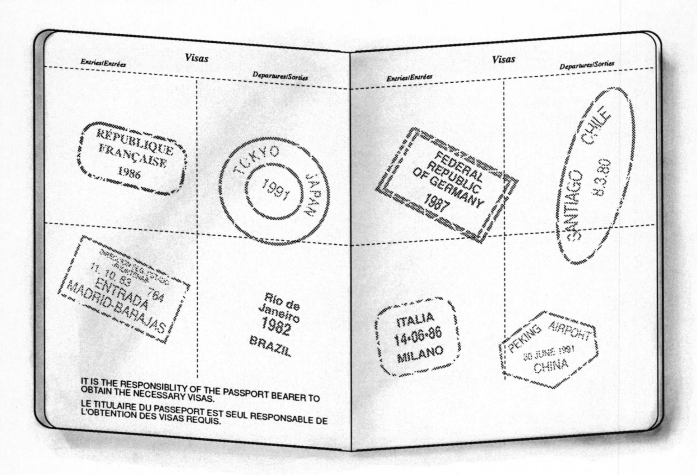

Victor:	I hear that you've traveled a lot, Mrs. Brennan. Have you ever been to Spain?
Mrs. Brennan:	Yes, I _have_ . I _____ there in 1983.
	1 2
Victor:	What about Portugal?
Mrs. Brennan:	No. I've _____ been there. But I was in _____ in 1982.
	3 4
Lynn:	Have you _____ been to China?
	5
Mrs. Brennan:	_____ , ____ _____ . In 1991. And I _____ in Japan that year, too.
	6 7 8 9
Pravit:	What about Thailand?
Mrs. Brennan:	I've _____ _____ there. But I would like to go.
	10 11
Olga:	_____ _____ _____ _____ ____ Chile?
	12 13 14 15 16
Mrs. Brennan:	Yes, I have. I was there in 1980. It's a beautiful country.

What's your opinion? Look at the pictures and complete the questions. Then answer the questions with *should* or *ought to* and give a reason for your opinion.

1. Should Frank and Gina buy a ____*big house*____ or a ____*small house*____?
They should buy a small house. Small houses are less expensive.

2. Should Lucy and Simon go to _____ or to _____ for their vacation?

_____

3. Should Victor and his wife go to _____ or to _____?

_____

4. Should Keiko and Lynn buy a _____ or a _____ for their

apartment?

_____

Complete these questions. Use *any, anyone (anybody), anywhere (anyplace),* or *anything.*

1. Do you know _____*any*_____ people in Los Angeles?

2. Do you know _____ about Texas?

3. Are you going _____ after class?

4. Are you going to speak to _____ on the phone tonight?

5. Do you have _____ friends in New York?

6. Have you ever complained about _____ in a department store?

Now answer the questions in exercise 2. Use your own information.

1. _____

2. _____

3. _____

4. _____

5. _____

6. _____

Look again at Ann Brennan's passport on page 26. Then complete the conversation.

A: Mrs. Brennan has been to France, __*hasn't*__ __*she*__ ?
      ¹   ²

B: _____ , _____ _____ .
   ³   ⁴   ⁵

A: She's been to Belgium, too, _____ _____ ?
                                ⁶   ⁷

B: ____ , _____ _____ .
   ⁸   ⁹   ¹⁰

A: What about Germany? She's _____ there, _____ _____ ?
                             ¹¹   ¹²   ¹³

B: _____ , _____ _____ .
   ¹⁴   ¹⁵   ¹⁶

A: She hasn't _____ to Thailand, _____ _____ ?
              ¹⁷   ¹⁸   ¹⁹

B: ____ , _____ _____ . But she's been to China.
   ²⁰   ²¹   ²²

A: Well, she sure _____ _____ to a lot of places, _____ _____ ?
                  ²³   ²⁴   ²⁵   ²⁶

B: _____ , _____ _____ . She loves to travel.
   ²⁷   ²⁸   ²⁹

EXERCISE 1

Complete the conversation. Use the words in the box.

| anything | ever | might | never | someplace | should |

Customer: I'd like to go ___someplace___ nice for my vacation next month.
1

Agent: How about Las Vegas? We have a special tour there. Have you _____

been there?
2

Customer: No. I've _____ been there, but I'd like to go _____
3   4

I can relax.

Agent: I see. What about Sanibel?

Customer: Well, I don't really know _____ about Sanibel. I've
5

_____ been there.
6

Agent: It's very beautiful. There are some gorgeous beaches and great restaurants.

Customer: Hmmm. That _____ be a good idea. _____ I make a
7   8

reservation right now?

Agent: Well, you still have some time. I'll give you a brochure to look at.

You _____ call me tomorrow if you have any questions.
9

EXERCISE 2

Match the part of the sentence on the left with the part on the right.

_e_ 1. If you go to France,   a. we ought to plan our vacation.

___ 2. He should visit the Empire State Building   b. if the class ends early.

___ 3. If we travel around Canada,   c. if he goes to New York.

___ 4. They ought to go to that movie about China   d. she ought to visit Madrid.

___ 5. If she goes to Spain,   e. you should see the Eiffel Tower.

___ 6. If I got some travel brochures,   f. we ought to go to Quebec City.

Pretend you are going on a one-week vacation. Look at the brochures. Where might you go? Why? Write a short letter to a friend about your possible plans.

Dear _____,
    I'm planning my next vacation. I'd like to go somewhere _____. The travel agent gave me some brochures. I haven't decided yet, but I might _____.

_____

_____

_____

_____

_____

_____

_____

_____

_____

EXERCISE 1

Look at the pictures. Write what the waiter is doing. Use the words in the box.

| pull down | put in | put on | take off | ~~take out~~ | turn off | turn on | write down |

1. *He is taking out* _____ the chicken.

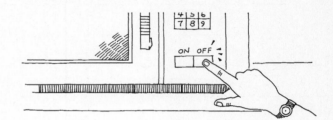

2. _____ the oven.

3. _____ his jacket.

4. _____ his jacket.

5. _____ the order.

6. _____ the shade.

7. _____ the chicken.

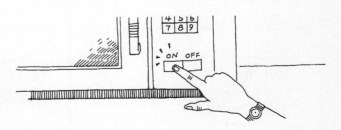

8. _____ the oven.

Put the pictures in exercise 1 in the correct order.

1. _Picture 3_

2. _____

3. _____

4. _____

5. _____

6. _____

7. _____

8. _____

Now write a paragraph describing what the waiter did. Use the words *first, next,* and *then.*

First the waiter put on his jacket. Next

_____

_____

_____

After that he went home.

What do these signs mean? Write what you think under each one. Begin with the word *No.*

1. _No Smoking_

2. _____

3. _____

4. _____

5. _____

6. _____

7. _____

8. _____

9. _____

This picture shows the class during a break. What was everyone doing? Complete the sentences.

1. Chico *was eating a sandwich* _____.

2. Lisa _____.

3. Mrs. Ford and Noriko _____.

4. Philip _____.

5. Maria and Akira _____.

6. Harry _____.

7. Juan _____.

8. Rodrigo _____.

Write sentences about the picture in exercise 1. Use *While*.

1. (Chico / Lisa) *While Chico was eating, Lisa was listening to the radio.*

2. (Mrs. Ford / Harry) _____

_____

3. (Akira / Juan) _____

_____

4. (Rodrigo / Philip) _____

_____

5. (Noriko / Maria) _____

_____

Match the sentences. Each sentence on the left gives the reason for an event on the right.

_f_ 1. She's very tired.

____ 2. She studied very hard.

____ 3. The music was very loud.

____ 4. The football game was very exciting.

____ 5. The camera was very expensive.

____ 6. She ate very quickly.

a. She got 100% on the test.

b. She wants to go again next week.

c. She didn't buy it.

d. She couldn't hear the phone.

e. She got a stomachache.

f. She's going to bed now.

Look at exercise 3. Combine the sentences that you matched. Use the word *so*.

1. *She's so tired that she's going to bed now.*

2. _____

3. _____

4. _____

5. _____

6. _____

Look again at the picture in exercise 1. Then complete the conversation.

Lisa: Look, Rodrigo took this picture with his new camera.

Mona: Not bad! Was Philip really _____*sleeping*_____ ?
1

Lisa: Yes, he _____ . He worked _____ hard the night before that he fell asleep
2   3

during the break.

Mona: Was Akira _____ an English magazine?
4

Lisa: _____ , he _____ . It was Spanish. Maria gave it to him.
5   6

Mona: I see. And _____ Maria and Akira _____ reading, Juan was writing
7   8

something. What was it? I can't see. Was he doing his homework?

Lisa: _____ , he _____ . He was writing a letter.
9   10

Mona: What were Noriko and Mrs. Ford _____ about?
11

Lisa: I don't know. I was _____ to some rock music. It was _____ noisy
12   13

that I couldn't hear anything else.

Complete this letter. Use the past continuous tense (*was/were doing*) or the simple past tense (*did*).

Dear Mom and Dad,

Today was not a good day. I **1 was jogging** (jog) near the park this morning, when I **2** _____ (see) a bad car accident. I immediately **3** _____ (look) for a phone. While I **4** _____ (call) the police, many other people **5** _____ (stop) to help. When the police **6** _____ (arrive) five minutes later, they got the man out of the car. He wasn't hurt badly, but his right leg **7** _____ (bleed). He was really lucky. He **8** _____ (wear) his seat belt when the accident **9** _____ (happen). The other car **10** _____ (drive) much faster than the speed limit.

Now complete and answer these questions about the accident.

1. The accident happened near the park, _____ *didn't it* _____ ?
   Yes, it did. _____

2. The police arrived quickly, _____ ?
   _____

3. The man wasn't hurt badly, _____ ?
   _____

4. His leg was bleeding, _____ ?
   _____

5. He wasn't wearing his seat belt, _____ ?
   _____

6. The other car was driving slowly, _____ ?
   _____

The paragraphs in this newspaper article are not in the right order. What is the correct order? Renumber the paragraphs.

(1) Rogers was driving along Kendall when he saw a boy on a bicycle. The boy was listening to a radio and not paying attention to traffic. Rogers had to stop his car immediately. When he stopped his car, Higgins, driving behind, hit Rogers. **(2)** Miami. Jan. 19. Yesterday morning at 8:30 A.M. there was a two-car accident at the corner of Kendall Drive and 107th Street. The two drivers, John Rogers of Miami and Mary Higgins of Boca Raton, are resting in Miami Hospital where doctors say they will stay until tomorrow.

(3) According to the police, many accidents happen because people do not pay attention to traffic. "It is not safe to read or listen to the radio when you are crossing the street or riding a bike. You must pay attention," says Ralph Rodriguez. The police hope fewer accidents will happen in the future.

(4) This was not the first accident to happen at Kendall and 107th St. Last month a car, driving faster than the speed limit, had to stop quickly when an elderly man was crossing the street. The man was reading the newspaper and did not see the car coming. The car did not hit the man, but he fell and broke his arm.

The correct order is: _____

Read these sentences about the newspaper article. Write *That's right, That's wrong,* or *It doesn't say.* Correct the sentences that are wrong.

1. The boy on the bicycle was listening to rock music.

   It doesn't say. _____

2. The two drivers are still in the hospital.

   _____

3. Rogers's car hit Higgins's car.

   _____

4. More than one accident has taken place at Kendall Dr. and 107th St.

   _____

5. Last month an elderly man broke his arm when a car hit him.

   _____

Complete this crossword puzzle.

Across

4. Buy

7. Pick _____

8. You can sit on this.

10. _____ Smoking!

12. ¢

13. It goes up and down.

16. Run / _____ / run

17. Same as 17 down

18. It's not your book; it's _____ book.

19. You can keep money in this.

21. Not dirty

22. A _____ding invitation

23. At the same time

26. Man (plural)

27. Take something that is not yours

28. I'm _____ tired that I'm going to bed.

29. You don't smoke, _____ you?

Down

1. Pravit's wife works here

2. _____ quiet!

3. People who help with a crime

5. Comes in

6. Look forward _____

9. His book and _____ book

11. Same as 9 down

14. Expensive

15. A banana, _____ apple

17. Would you like coffee _____ tea?

20. Old

22. _____chair

23. Past of *is*

24. I am (contraction)

25. Finish

EXERCISE 1

Look at the pictures. Write a sentence about each one. Use *was(n't) able to* or *were(n't) able to*.

1. Olga / put up the window shades

Olga was able to put up the window shades.

2. Pierre / fix the bicycle

_____

_____

3. Oscar / finish the English test

_____

_____

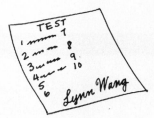

4. Lynn / finish the English test

_____

_____

5. Lucy and Simon / go on vacation

_____

_____

6. Keiko and Lynn / clean the kitchen

_____

_____

Complete these questions. Use *you* and the correct tense of *be able to*.

1. *Will you be able to* _____ relax tomorrow?

2. _____ understand this exercise?

3. _____ speak a lot of English since you began this class?

4. _____ speak English when you were a child?

5. _____ take a vacation next year?

6. If _____ not _____ take a vacation next year, when

   _____ take one?

7. _____ fix a radio?

8. _____ see any of your friends last weekend?

9. _____ usually _____ get up early in the morning?

10. _____ get enough sleep so far this week?

What about you? Answer the questions in exercise 2. Use your own information.

1. _____

2. _____

3. _____

4. _____

5. _____

6. _____

7. _____

8. _____

9. _____

10. _____

Look at the pictures. Make statements about the people. Use an appropriate reflexive pronoun (-self/-selves) and the words under the pictures.

1. (cut) *She cut herself.*

2. (enjoy) _____

3. (burn) _____

4. (hurt) _____

Complete these statements by using the appropriate reflexive pronouns (-self/-selves).

1. I can't help you, Juan. You'll have to do your homework by _____ *yourself* _____ .

2. Maria and Chico didn't join us. They sat in the back of the room by _____ .

3. Pravit didn't enjoy _____ at the class party.

4. Her secretary wasn't there. She had to answer the phone _____ .

5. Now that our children are grown, we live by _____ .

6. I looked at _____ in the mirror.

7. The little kitten sits by _____ in the corner.

Match the reasons on the left with the results on the right.

_e_ 1. She was very sick.   a. She couldn't buy it.

___ 2. The soup was very hot.   b. She wasn't on time for work.

___ 3. The dress was very expensive.   c. They couldn't sleep.

___ 4. The boy was very young.   d. She wasn't able to lift the box.

___ 5. They were very hungry.   e. She didn't go to school.

___ 6. She was very confused.   f. She didn't answer the question.

___ 7. He is very angry.   g. I couldn't eat it.

___ 8. They were very excited.   h. He wasn't able to see the movie.

___ 9. She got up very late.   i. He hasn't spoken to me.

___ 10. The woman was very weak.   j. They couldn't wait for dinner.

Combine the sentences that you matched in exercise 6. Use _too . . . to_ + verb.

1. _She was too sick to go to school._

2. _____

3. _____

4. _____

5. _____

6. _____

7. _____

8. _____

9. _____

10. _____

EXERCISE 1

Complete the conversation with the correct adjective form (*-ed* or *-ing*). Use *bore, exhaust, interest,* or *surprise.*

Keiko: Did you hear about Lee's surprise party?

Lynn: No. How was it? Was he really _____*surprised*_____ ?

1

Keiko: Yeah, he was. He didn't expect anything.

Lynn: A surprise party is a lot of work, isn't it?

Keiko: Yes. His son organized the party. He worked so hard that he was really

_____ by 8:00.

2

Lynn: And what about you? Did you have a good time? Did you meet any

_____ people?

3

Keiko: Well, you know how parties are. Some people were _____ ; some

4

were _____ . One man told me a very long story about his cat.

5

I was too _____ to even pay attention!

6

EXERCISE 2

THINGS TO DO

✓ buy Isabel shoes
✓ give Eddie $5.00
give Isabel lunch
✓ get Eddie a new jacket
find Grandma a gift
✓ write to my sister
make Hector dinner
show Hector the letter
from my sister

Look at Olga's list of things to do. What has she done? What hasn't she done? Write sentences. Use *for* and *to* in your answers.

1. *She's bought shoes for Isabel.*

2. _____

3. _____

4. _____

5. _____

6. _____

7. _____

8. _____

Look at the pictures. What are the people doing?

1. *They're cutting each other's hair.*

2. _____

3. _____

4. _____

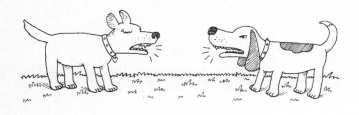

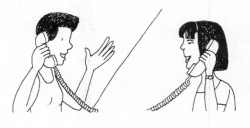

5. _____

6. _____

Circle the correct response.

1. Isabel looks tired.
   a. Yeah, she's exhausted.
   b. Yeah, she's exhausting.

2. If you help me, I'll help you.
   a. It's a deal.
   b. Yes, I will.

3. Could you make me a sandwich?
   a. Here.
   b. Sure.

4. He writes to her and she writes to him.
   a. Yeah. They write to themselves all the time.
   b. Yeah. They write to each other all the time.

44 UNIT 6

Complete the conversation with appropriate words.

Woman: *How* was the movie?
        ₁

Man: I didn't like it. The story wasn't very _____ .
                                                  ₂

Woman: I'm sorry you _____ disappointed.
                   ₃

Man: Me too. I didn't _____ myself at all.
                  ₄

Woman: Who did you go with?

Man: I went by _____ . . . . How was the museum?
                ₅

Woman: We were fascinated. The paintings were very _____ .
                                                        ₆

Man: I'm glad you enjoyed _____ .
                            ₇

Woman: We are, too.

Man: _____ did you go with?
     ₈

Woman: My husband and I went by _____ . . . . And how was that new
                                             ₉

restaurant you went to?

Man: I was _____ . The food _____ exciting at all.
                 ₁₀   ₁₁

Woman: Who did you go _____ ?
                    ₁₂

Man: I went with my girlfriend.

Unscramble the words on the left. Then match them with their opposites on the right.

g 1. legsin   *single*   a. young

____ 2. dinsie   b. part time

____ 3. yelredl   c. outside

____ 4. lulf mite   d. leisure-time activities

____ 5. ta mohe   e. boring

____ 6. tilsersponsiebii   f . at work

____ 7. gintresetin   g. married

Complete this questionnaire about life styles. Use your own information.

LIFE-STYLES PROFILE

1. I always enjoy myself when _____.

2. I think _____ is exciting.

3. I feel bored when _____.

4. I think the idea of security is _____.

5. I'm not interested in _____.

6. Doing chores around the house is _____.

7. I find _____ exhausting.

8. My favorite leisure-time activity is _____.

9. I worry a lot about _____.

10. I prefer to _____ by myself.

11. I think it's important that people _____ each other.

12. I prefer to live in a (n) _____.

LESSON
1

Linda and Larry are at a restaurant. Circle the correct word in parentheses to complete their conversation.

Larry: You look (**1.** (beautiful) / beautifully) tonight, Linda.

Linda: Thanks, Larry. This is a great restaurant! The food tastes (**2.** good / well), and the band sounds (**3.** terrific / terrifically) .

Larry: Yeah. They really play (**4.** beautiful / beautifully), don't they? Hey, would you like to dance?

Linda: Sure.

Larry: It feels (**5.** nice / nicely) to dance again. You know, I haven't danced with you since our wedding.

Linda: Be careful! Those people are really dancing (**6.** bad / badly) .

Larry: You're right. They look (**7.** dangerous / dangerously) .

Linda: Ouch, my toe! Let's sit down.

Larry: Good idea. How about some coffee? The people next to us just got coffee, and it smells (**8.** wonderful / wonderfully) .

Linda: That sounds (**9.** nice / nicely) .

Isabel has drawn pictures of some of the people in her mother's English class. Who are they? Write the correct name under each picture.

| Gina | Lucy | Oscar | Roberto |
| Keiko | ~~Olga~~ | Pierre | Victor |

1. _It looks like Olga._

2. _____

3. _____

4. _____

5. _____

6. _____

7. _____

8. _____

Who do you think this is?

9. _____

Look at the picture. Then complete the conversation. Use *have (not) got*. Use contractions if possible.

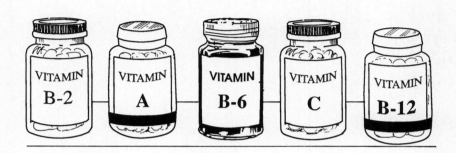

Lucy: Excuse me. I'm having trouble finding some of the vitamins I need.

Can you help me?

Manager: Sure. What are you looking for?

Lucy: __Have__ you __got__ any Vitamin A?
　　　　　1　　　　2

Manager: Let's see. I'm sure we ____ _____ Vitamin A. Yes, there it is, between
　　　　　　　　　　　　　　　3　　4

the B-2 and B-6.

Lucy: And what about B-1? I don't have much at home, and I don't see any

on the shelf.

Manager: Sorry. We're out of B-1. But we ____ _____ B-12.
　　　　　　　　　　　　　　　　　　5　　6

Lucy: Thanks, but I ____ _____ plenty of B-12 at home. I'll take a bottle
　　　　　　　　　7　　8

of B-2 though. _____ you _____ any Vitamin C?
　　　　　　　　　9　　　　　10

Manager: Yes. Right over there. Anything else?

Lucy: How about Vitamin E?

Manager: We _____ _____ Vitamin E.
　　　　　　　　　11　　　　　12

Lucy: And Vitamin D?

Manager: We _____ _____ any Vitamin D either.
　　　　　　　　　13　　　　　14

Read the conversation in exercise 3 again and cross off the items Lucy bought.

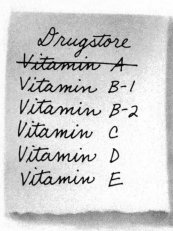

Drugstore
~~Vitamin A~~
Vitamin B-1
Vitamin B-2
Vitamin C
Vitamin D
Vitamin E

What does Lucy have? What does she still need? Now answer these questions.
Use *plenty of* or *not enough*.

1. Does Lucy have enough Vitamin A?

   Yes. She has plenty of Vitamin A.

2. What about B-1?

   She doesn't have enough.

3. B-2?

   _____

4. B-12?

   _____

5. Vitamin C?

   _____

6. Vitamin D?

   _____

7. Vitamin E?

   _____

EXERCISE 1

Complete these sentences with *a* or *an* (only when necessary).

1. What   _Ø_   delicious soup!

2. What   _a_   funny movie!

3. What _____ hot day!

4. What _____ loud music!

5. What _____ exhausting day!

6. What _____ sad song!

7. What _____ embarrassing story!

8. What _____ terrible coffee!

EXERCISE 2

Match the sentences in exercise 1 with the people who said them.

1. _Sentence 3_____

2. _____

3. _____

4. _____

5. _____

6. _____

7. _____

8. _____

Complete these questions. Use a *negative* verb.

1. __*aren't*__ you feeling OK today?

2. _____ you be in class tomorrow?

3. _____ you at home last night?

4. _____ you able to do your work?

5. _____ you ever eaten carrot cake?

6. _____ you like ice cream?

Answer the questions in exercise 3. Use your own information.

1. _____

2. _____

3. _____

4. _____

5. _____

6. _____

What's wrong with these things? Write sentences with *too* or *so*. Follow the examples.

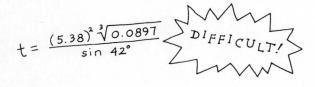

1. _*It's too dirty to wear.*_
   *It's so dirty I can't wear it.*

2. _____

   _____

3. _____

   _____

4. _____

   _____

Read this recipe for tomato soup. Then read the statements and write *That's right, That's wrong,* or *It doesn't say.* Correct the sentences that are wrong.

TOMATO SOUP

1 small onion, chopped   1 tablespoon butter
1 red or green pepper, chopped   1 tablespoon flour
1/2 pound fresh tomatoes   2 teaspoons red wine
2 cups water   salt and black pepper

Cook the chopped onion and pepper in the butter for 6 minutes. Add the flour and mix well. Heat the water and add it very slowly to the onion and pepper mixture. Cut the tomatoes and add them to the soup. Cook very slowly for 15 minutes. Add plenty of black pepper and salt. Then add the wine.

1. You have to chop the onion.

   That's right. _____

2. It's OK to use tomatoes from a can.

   _____

3. You can use green pepper or red pepper.

   _____

4. You cook the onion and pepper in wine.

   _____

5. This recipe is for four people.

   _____

6. You add cold water to the onion and pepper mixture.

   _____

7. This recipe takes about 30 minutes to make.

   _____

8. This soup will taste sweet.

   _____

Unscramble these names of snack foods. Then check the correct column.

		Sweet	Sour	Salty
1. sairsin	_raisins_	✔	☐	☐
2. stun	_____	☐	☐	☐
3. nagroe ceiju	_____	☐	☐	☐
4. triuf	_____	☐	☐	☐
5. cei mreac	_____	☐	☐	☐
6. toptoa phics	_____	☐	☐	☐
7. melondea	_____	☐	☐	☐
8. sokocie	_____	☐	☐	☐
9. roppcon	_____	☐	☐	☐
10. dancy	_____	☐	☐	☐
11. umg	_____	☐	☐	☐
12. amj	_____	☐	☐	☐
13. tubtre	_____	☐	☐	☐

EXERCISE 1

Read Carlos's composition about Colombia. Complete it with *the* when appropriate.

Before I came to __*the*__ United States, I lived in _____ Colombia. _____ Colombia is in
$\quad\quad$ 1 $\quad\quad\quad\quad\quad\quad\quad\quad\quad\quad\quad$ 2 $\quad\quad\quad\quad\quad\quad$ 3

_____ South America. _____ Panama is to the northwest. _____ Ecuador and _____ Peru
4 $\quad\quad\quad\quad\quad\quad$ 5 $\quad\quad\quad\quad\quad\quad\quad\quad\quad\quad\quad\quad\quad$ 6 $\quad\quad\quad\quad\quad\quad\quad\quad\quad$ 7

are to the south, and _____ Brazil and _____ Venezuela are to the east. _____ Bogota is the
$\quad\quad\quad\quad\quad\quad\quad$ 8 $\quad\quad\quad\quad\quad\quad$ 9 $\quad\quad\quad\quad\quad\quad\quad\quad\quad\quad\quad$ 10

country's largest city.

_____ Pacific Ocean lies to the west, and _____ Caribbean Sea is to the north. _____
11 $\quad\quad\quad\quad\quad\quad\quad\quad\quad\quad\quad\quad\quad\quad$ 12 $\quad\quad\quad\quad\quad\quad\quad\quad\quad\quad\quad\quad\quad$ 13

Andes Mountains run through the country from north to south.

Colombia's largest river is _____ Magdalena River. There are no very large lakes (such as
$\quad\quad\quad\quad\quad\quad\quad\quad\quad\quad\quad$ 14

_____ Lake Superior in _____ United States), and there are no deserts (such as _____
15 $\quad\quad\quad\quad\quad\quad\quad\quad\quad$ 16 $\quad\quad\quad\quad\quad\quad\quad\quad\quad\quad\quad\quad\quad\quad\quad\quad$ 17

Sahara in _____ Africa).
$\quad\quad\quad\quad$ 18

EXERCISE 2

Read Carlos's composition again. Then look at the map. Fill in the blanks with the
correct names.

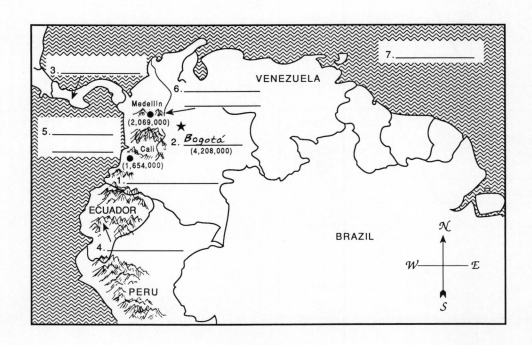

Complete the questions for this geography quiz.

1. Which is _____the highest mountain_____ in the world?

   (a.) Mt. Everest.   b. Mt. McKinley.   c. Mt. Kilimanjaro.

2. Which is _____ in the world?

   a. The Atlantic.   b. The Pacific.   c. The Indian.

3. Which is _____ in the world?

   a. The Nile.   b. The Chang Jiang.   c. The Amazon.

4. Which is _____ in the world?

   a. The Gobi.   b. The Sahara.   c. Death Valley.

5. Which is _____ in the world?

   a. Luxembourg.   b. Vatican City.   c. Liechtenstein.

Look at the pictures. Make comparisons.

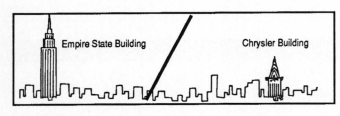

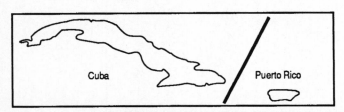

1. _The Empire State Building is taller than the Chrysler Building._

2. _____

3. _____

4. _____

EXERCISE 1

Match the numbers on the left with the words on the right.

d 1. 0.25   a. two hundred (and) fifty

___ 2. 2.5   b. ten and twenty-five hundredths

___ 3. 25.2   c. twenty-five million

___ 4. 10.25   d. twenty-five (one) hundredths

___ 5. 250   e. twenty-five and two-tenths

___ 6. 2,500   f. twenty-five thousand

___ 7. 2,500,000   g. two and five-tenths

___ 8. 25,000   h. two thousand five hundred

___ 9. 25,000,000   i. one thousand twenty-five

___ 10. 1,025   j. two million five hundred thousand

EXERCISE 2

Look at the pictures and complete the conversations.

the Eiffel Tower

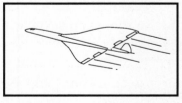
the Great Wall

1. A: *How tall is the Eiffel Tower?*

   B: 1,056 feet.

2. A: _____

   B: 2,150 miles.

the Mayan ruins

the Concorde jet

3. A: _____

   B: More than 1,000 years.

4. A: _____

   B: More than 1,000 mph.

Dom Perignon champagne

5. A: _____

   B: More than $60.

Look at the chart. Then read the statements. Write *That's right, That's wrong,* or *It doesn't say.* Correct the statements that are wrong.

Lakes of the World			
	How large? (square miles)	How long? (miles)	How deep? (feet)
Albert	2,075	100	168
Baykal	12,162	395	5,315
Caspian Sea	143,244	760	3,363
Erie	9,910	241	210
Gairdner	1,840	90	...
Maracaibo	5,217	133	115
Ontario	7,550	193	802
Reindeer	2,568	143	720
Tanganyika	12,700	420	4,823

Source: Geological Survey, U.S. Interior Department, as published in *The World Almanac* (1989).

1. According to the chart, the Caspian Sea is the longest and largest lake in the world.

   That's right.
   _____

2. Lake Ontario is larger than Lake Erie.

   _____

3. Lake Tanganyika is the deepest lake.

   _____

4. Lake Maracaibo is one thousand fifteen feet deep.

   _____

5. Lake Albert is two thousand seventy-five square miles large.

   _____

6. Lake Reindeer is deeper than Lake Gairdner.

   _____

Now complete these sentences with information you didn't know before you saw the chart in exercise 3.

1. I didn't know that _____ .

2. I had no idea that _____ .

3. I just learned that _____ .

Complete this magazine article with the appropriate words.

Just _How_ Big Are They?
1

Russia is the _____ country in the world.
2

Vatican City is the _____ . Just how _____
3   4

are they? Russia is 6,593,000 _____ miles, and
5

Vatican City ____ .17 square mile – that is, seventeen one-
6

hundredths of a square mile.

The _____ is the longest river in the _____ . It
7   8

flows through east Africa to _____ Mediterranean Sea.
9

The _____ freshwater lake is Lake Superior
10

between _____ United States and Canada. The deepest
11

_____ is Lake Baykal in Russia. The _____
12   13

Desert in Africa is the largest desert. These are some of the

natural wonders of the _____ .
14

Many _____ incredible wonders were built by
15

people. For example, the tallest _____ is
16

the Sears Tower in Chicago. It's big _____ to hold
17

16,700 people. The _____ wall is the Great Wall
18

of China. How tall ____ the Sears Tower, and how
19

_____ is the Great Wall?
20

Unscramble these geographical names of places in the world. Then check the correct column.

		Country	State	City
1. danaca	_Canada_	✓	☐	☐
2. wiahai	_____	☐	☐	☐
3. zablir	_____	☐	☐	☐
4. ladsal	_____	☐	☐	☐
5. saxet	_____	☐	☐	☐
6. canih	_____	☐	☐	☐
7. koyot	_____	☐	☐	☐
8. nashhaig	_____	☐	☐	☐
9. nitacav yict	_____	☐	☐	☐

Cross out the word in each line that doesn't belong. Then write that word in the correct location.

1. Tokyo   Los Angeles   ~~Texas~~   _____

2. Amazon   Japan   Nile   _____

3. Andes   Rio Grande   Rocky Mts.   _____

4. Italy   Miami   Canada   _____

5. California   Alaska   Himalayas   _Texas_

UNIT 9

LESSON 1

EXERCISE 1

What kinds of products are grown or made in Western Europe? Look at the map. Make sentences with the words in parentheses and the verbs in the box.

| grow | mine |
| make | produce |

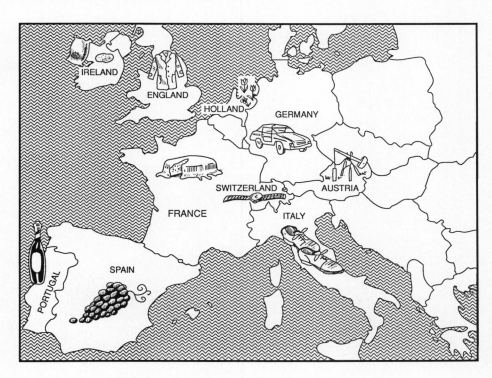

1. (shoes) _Shoes are made in Italy._

2. (grapes) _____

3. (cheese) _____

4. (wine) _____

5. (watches) _____

6. (cars) _____

7. (oil) _____

8. (raincoats) _____

9. (potatoes) _____

10. (flowers) _____

Gina wrote this letter to her friend Emilia. Complete it with *before, after, during,* and *for.*

Dear Emilia,

Hi! How are things at home? It's now a few weeks

_____*after*_____ the wedding. It was wonderful!
1

_____ the wedding we were so busy that we
2

couldn't relax. There was so much to do -- the invitations,

the food, the band. But our friends helped us a lot.

I really missed you. I often thought of you

_____ the reception. All of my new friends
3

were there, but not any of my friends from Italy.

_____ the reception, Frank and I left for a
4

short trip. We really enjoyed ourselves. Now we're back in

Dallas. I'm still working and going to school. I have English

class at 6:30. _____ class I always meet Frank
5

_____ dinner at 8:00.
6

What about you? What are you doing these days?

Please write.

Love,

Gina

Dr. Alvarez is with a patient. Look at his notes and complete his advice. Use *you'd better (not)*.

Ralph Rodriguez
male, 58 years old
200 lbs (should be 150 lbs)
smokes
drinks
doesn't exercise
very nervous—works 12 hours a day
sleeps only 5 hrs a night
should have blood test
want to see him again next month

1. _____*you'd better not*_____ smoke.

2. _____ exercise every day.

3. _____ work so much.

4. _____ get more sleep.

5. _____ relax.

6. _____ eat less.

7. _____ eat ice cream and cake.

8. _____ eat vegetables.

9. _____ take vitamins.

10. _____ keep snacks at home.

11. _____ get upset at work.

12. _____ have a blood test.

13. _____ listen to my advice.

14. _____ see me again in a month.

Ralph is in a restaurant. He decided to eat a healthy meal. Look at the pictures and complete his thoughts.

1. _I'd better have the salad._

2. _____

_____

3. _____

_____

4. _____

_____

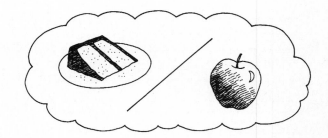

5. _____

_____

Look at the chart. Then read the statements. Write *That's right, That's wrong,* or *It doesn't say.*
Correct the statements that are wrong.

Building	Location	Year	Architect
Empire State Building	N.Y.C.	1929–31	Shreves, Lamp, & Hartman
Guggenheim Museum	N.Y.C.	1956–59	Frank Lloyd Wright
Lincoln Memorial	Washington, D.C.	1914–17	Henry Bacon
Sears Tower	Chicago	1970–74	Skidmore, Owings, & Merrill
St. Patrick's Cathedral	N.Y.C.	1858–79	James Renwick
World Trade Center	N.Y.C.	1962–72	Minoru Yamasaki

1. The Sears Tower was completed before the Empire State Building.

   That's wrong. It was completed after the Empire State Building.

2. The Lincoln Memorial was designed by Frank Lloyd Wright.

   _____

3. The World Trade Center was built in 11 years.

   _____

4. Four of the buildings were built in the same city.

   _____

5. The Lincoln Memorial was completed before the Empire State Building was begun.

   _____

6. St. Patrick's Cathedral was designed by the same architect who designed the Sears Tower.

   _____

7. The Sears Tower was named after a businessman.

   _____

Complete the conversations.

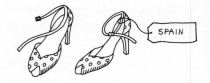

1. A: _What nice earrings !_
   B: _Thanks. They were_
   made in Mexico.

2. A: _____
   B: _____

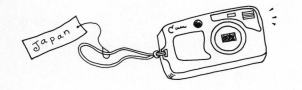

3. A: _____
   B: _____
   _____

4. A: _____
   B: _____
   _____

5. A: _____
   B: _____
   _____

6. A: _____
   B: _____
   _____

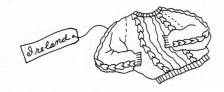

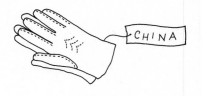

7. A: _____
   B: _____
   _____

8. A: _____
   B: _____
   _____

Complete the tour guide's descriptions with appropriate words.

Good morning, ladies and gentlemen. Today's tour _is_ called the President's Tour. We're
                                              1
going ____ visit the monuments and buildings that _____ dedicated to some of our most
      2   3
famous presidents.

First we'll stop at the Washington Monument. It was _____ in 1884. It is
                                                          4
dedicated to our first _____ , George Washington, and it is 555 feet _____ .
                              5   6
You can take the _____ , or you can climb to the top — but there are 898 steps!
                        7
Next we'll _____ the White House, the official home of our present president. It was
                 8
_____ by James Hoban. The first building was burned ____ the British in the
       9   10
War of 1812, but it was rebuilt and _____ white in 1818.
                                           11
Next we'll stop at the John F. Kennedy Center. It was _____ in 1971 and _____
                                                            12   13
$73 million. It is 630 feet long and 300 feet wide.

Read the tour guide's description in exercise 1 and answer the questions. Give short answers.

1. Why is the tour called the President's Tour?

   Because all the monuments and buildings are dedicated to presidents.

2. Who lives in the White House?

   _____

3. Why is it called the White House?

   _____

4. Which of the buildings on the tour is the newest?

   _____

5. Which is the oldest?

   _____

6. Which of the buildings or monuments is the highest?

   _____

Trivia Quiz. First complete the sentences. Then answer them.

1. The World Trade Center was designed *by*
   a. Frank Lloyd Wright.
   b. Minoru Yamasaki. (circled)
   c. James Renwick.

2. _____ was Don Quixote written by?
   a. William Shakespeare.
   b. Jane Austen.
   c. Miguel Cervantes.

3. When was the telephone _____ ?
   a. In 1776.
   b. In 1876.
   c. In 1976.

4. Vitamin C was _____ in
   a. 1712.
   b. 1812.
   c. 1912.

5. The Lincoln Memorial is _____ of
   a. glass.
   b. marble.
   c. plastic.

6. _____ was the electric battery invented?
   a. Italy.
   b. U.S.A.
   c. Germany.

Unscramble these words. You can find all nine of these things in Washington, D.C.

1. strethae   T H E A (T) E R S
2. thloes   _ ◯ _ _ _ _
3. rakps   _ _ _ _ ◯
4. sumusem   _ ◯ _ _ _ _ _
5. tresraustan _ _ _ _ _ ◯ _ _ _ _
6. nomstumne   _ _ _ _ _ _ _ _ ◯
7. tsueats   _ ◯ _ _ _ _ _
8. ginstapin   _ _ ◯ _ _ _ _ _ _

Now unscramble the letters in the circles above.

9. __ __ __ __ __ __ __ __

EXERCISE 1

Fill in the missing words.

Adjectives	**Adverbs**
1. inexpensive	*inexpensively*
2. _____	well
3. fast	_____
4. _____	slowly
5. hard	_____

EXERCISE 2

Fill in the blanks with the appropriate words from the chart in exercise 1.

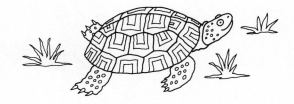

1. A turtle moves *slowly* _____ .

2. A jet is _____ .

3. This sweater isn't _____ .

4. You can't eat _____ here.

5. Lucy did very _____ on her test.

6. Pierre didn't study very _____ .

UNIT 10   **69**

Complete these conversations with advice.

1. **Keiko:** I've got a headache.

    Lynn: *If I were you, I'd take an aspirin.*

2. **Pravit:** I don't know where to go during the school break.

    Tony: _____

    _____

3. **Customer:** Should I get the steak or the chicken?

    Pierre: _____

    _____

4. **Simon:** I'm going to the store.

    Lucy: It looks like rain. _____

    _____

5. **Patient:** I have a terrible cough.

    Oscar: _____

    _____

6. **Jerry:** I finally finished painting the garage.

    Ann: You look exhausted. _____

    _____

7. **Roberto:** How much money should I take with me?

    Victor: _____

    _____

8. **Frank:** I have to get my aunt a birthday present. Any ideas?

    You: _____

    _____

Complete the conversation with the verbs given.

Olga: Well, it's the school break again. What do you plan _to do_ ?
                                                            1 do

Lynn: I really want _____ a car. I'd like _____ to Los Angeles.
                                         2 buy   **3** drive

Olga: That sounds like a nice idea. Have you _____ there before?
                                                             4 be

Lynn: No, but I have a friend there.

Olga: Well, if I _____ you, I _____ La Jolla. You know, it's not far from L.A.
                                  5 be   **6** visit

and it's really beautiful.

Lynn: I know. I'd like _____ to San Diego, too. I hear they have a great zoo.
                                           7 go

Olga: They do. I'd definitely _____ to the zoo. In fact, I _____ it!
                                              8 go   **9** not miss

Complete these sentences about camping. Use your own information.

1. If I went camping, _____ .

2. If I didn't have a backpack, _____ .

3. If I were broke, _____ .

4. If I were all alone, _____ .

5. If I heard an unusual noise, _____ .

6. If I felt sick, _____ .

7. I'd be very upset if _____ .

8. I'd enjoy myself a lot better if _____ .

9. I'd go home if _____ .

10. I wouldn't go camping if _____ .

Circle the appropriate response.

1. I plan to go camping. How about you?
   a. Thanks. I'd like to very much.
   b. Camping is fun.
   c. I'm going to Miami.

2. If I were you, I'd fly.
   a. Yes, you were.
   b. No, you weren't.
   c. I think you're right.

3. I don't think camping is economical.
   a. What do you mean?
   b. Besides, it's cheap.
   c. Yes, you are.

4. Flying is quick.
   a. Besides, it's fast.
   b. Besides, it's dangerous.
   c. Besides, it's safe.

5. Should I stay one week or two?
   a. Yes, you should.
   b. If I were you, I'd stay two weeks.
   c. No, not at all.

6. I wouldn't go in the winter.
   a. Why not?
   b. Besides, it's very cold.
   c. Did you have a good time?

Look at the pictures. Complete the statements with *must* (for a conclusion), *might* (for a possibility), and *should* (for advice).

1. He ___*must*___ be tired.

2. He _____ lose some weight.

3. Arlene _____ be married.

4. Dr. Lopez _____ not be a man.

5. This student _____ study more.

6. This student _____ study a lot.

Look at this picture. Complete the sentences.

1. She might _____ or she might _____ .

2. In any case, she must _____ .

3. I think she should _____ .

Look at this consumer report about three air conditioners.

better → worse ● → ● → ○	**AirCool**	**Frosters**	**Coldpoint**
price	$269	$306	$243
weight (lbs)	8.5	9.0	7.5
cooling time	○	●	●
cooling efficiency	●	●	○
noise level	●	○	●

Now complete these sentences. Use the information above and the words in parentheses.

1. (quiet) The Coldpoint runs _more quietly than_ the _Frosters_ .

2. (efficient) The AirCool cools _____ _____ _____ the

   _____ .

3. (fast) The _____ cools a room _____ _____ of all three.

4. (cheap) You can buy the _____ _____ _____ _____

   the AirCool.

5. (slow) Of all three air conditioners, the _____ cools a room _____ _____

   _____ .

6. (easy) Because of its weight, you can carry the _____ _____ _____

   _____ the AirCool.

7. (quick) The _____ also cools _____ _____ _____ the AirCool

   or the _____ .

Look again at the report in exercise 3. Which air conditioner would YOU buy? Why?

_____

_____

_____

EXERCISE 1

Before you look at the statistics from the table below, answer this question: How can you travel the most safely in the United States?

_____

What do you think? Put these vehicles in the correct order. (1 = the safest)

___ car   ___ train

___ bus   ___ airplane

Now look at the table. Did you guess correctly?

Transportation Accident Passenger Death Rates, 1987

kind of transportation	passenger miles (billions)	passenger deaths	average death rate (per 1 million passenger miles)
cars and taxis	2,571.1	23,587	0.96
buses	141.3	50	0.04
trains	12.1	16	0.07
airplanes	329.1	252	0.03

Source: National Safety Council as published in *The World Almanac* (1989).

Look at the table again. Answer these questions.

1. According to the table, which type of transportation do Americans use most often?

   Cars and taxis.

2. How can you travel more safely, by bus or train?

   _____

3. How can you travel the most safely in the U.S.?

   _____

4. According to the table, which is the most dangerous form of transportation?

   _____

There are seven mistakes in this letter. Can you find and correct them?

Dear Nancy,

Well, it's school break again! ~~I~~ I'd like to go away this time, but I don't want go alone. Would you go with me if I pay for our transportation? Maybe we could rent a car and drive to Miami. I know you really enjoy to be on the beach. Or, maybe we could fly there and then rent a car. That way we can get there more fast and spend more time in the sun. I've read that you can rent a car cheap in Florida, so if we got an inexpensive flight, we would probably be able to do the whole trip pretty economical.

Ronnie tells me that you've really been working hard. If I was you, I'd take a break and go away with me! We'd have a great time. Let me know soon.

Love,

Which word doesn't belong? Cross it out.

1. car   motorcycle   ~~plane~~   truck

2. economically   slowly   easy   well

3. must   want   might   should

4. trip   passenger   man   driver

5. vehicle   motorcycle   truck   bus

6. people   women   person   men